© Saltire Music 2000

ISBN 0 94686!

Published in Great Bri
Saltire Music, 17 Harrison Garden

D0581079

Second Impression 2002
Third Impression 2004

The publishers are members of the Performing Right Society Ltd and the Mechanical Copyright Protection Society Ltd. Permission to use the above copyright material for performance or recording should be respectively addressed to these agencies.

Acknowledgements:
Highland Cathedral © 1982 Edition Roma/MCA Music GmbH
Universal/MCA Music Limited, 77 Fulham Palace Road, London W6
Used by permission of Music Sales Ltd
All Rights Reserved. International Copyright Secured

Printed in Great Britain by David Macdonald Ltd, Edinburgh

SONG TITLES

BLUE EYES

VERSE 1.
I left my loved ones so far away
with nothing but tears in their eyes.
Though our words spoke of promises, fear filled our hearts,
as we said our last good-byes.
Now, my work here's almost over
soon I'll be making my way.
Others may choose to remain here,
but I know, I could not stay.

CHORUS
For those blue eyes are pulling me homeward
like those blue skies above.
It's the voice of my memory that's calling.
It's the voice of love.
And when I'm home again,
be it sunshine or rain,
I'll be there in my own paradise.
For there she will be, for the whole world to see,
with those blue, blue eyes.

VERSE 2.
With work hard to come by and money so scarce,
I had no choice but to leave.
To the great land of fortune with beauty so rare
that no-one would ever believe.
But beauty is but in the eye, so it's said,
and, sometimes, is only skin deep.
And I have a vision of beauty
shining through the darkness of sleep.

CHORUS

*So often in the past, my work has taken me away from home for long
periods of time and, sometimes, I can relate to the many Scottish
emigrants who long to return to their home in Scotland, for one reason or
another. My reason is for the love of my family, all of whom, have Blue
Eyes.*

3

BLUE EYES

4

CUMNAROONANA

VERSE 1.

A penny for your thoughts, sir. A penny for your thoughts.
A penny for the dream that, I see, is in your eye.
Oh my thoughts are not for telling
and my dreams are not for selling,
so I'll not take your money, sir, for nothing can it buy.

CHORUS
Cumnaroonana, nara, cumnaroonanay na,
Cumnaroonana, nara, cumnaroonanay.

VERSE 2.

A piece of shining silver, a sovereign of gold.
All this I will give if your secret will be told.
If my secret, I tell you, then what will it be?
A secret no longer, no keep your bribery.

CHORUS

VERSE 3.

What, then, will you take, sir, that I can sacrifice?
What more can I offer? Come, man, name your price!
Your hand, sir, in friendship, I'll take nothing less.
For that is the secret of my happiness.

CHORUS

An incidental song based on the theory that money does not bring happiness. It is the conversation between two men. One, although very rich, is restless, nervy, and keen to know the secret of the other, who is peaceful, contented, and quite poor.

The chorus has no real meaning and is akin to mouth music.

Words and Music
by Ben Kelly

CUMNAROONANA

Arranged by
Alan Kitchen

9

HIGHLAND CRADLE SONG

VERSE 1.

Hush now, don't cry, my bairnie.
What tears are these that keep ye from sleep?
Lie still, in peace, my bairnie.
Hush now, and don't ye weep.

CHORUS

The nightingale sings,
o'er moorland it brings
a song on its' wings,
in the silence of night.
The mountain so tall,
the field-mouse so small,
in slumber, will fall,
till morning light.

VERSE 2.

Hush now, don't cry, my bairnie.
What makes ye sad and wantin' tae weep?
Dream happy dreams, my bairnie,
safe in your silent sleep.

CHORUS

This is an irresistible melody, traditionally known as a pipe tune but lends itself to the perfect lullaby.

Words by
Ben Kelly

HIGHLAND CRADLE SONG

Music Trad.
Arranged by
Alan Kitchen

13

night- ing ale sings, o'er moor-land it brings a song on its'
wings, in the si- lence of night. The moun- tain so tall the
field mouse so small, in slum- ber will fall, till morn- ning
light. si- lent sleep.

D.C. al Fine

rall...

FOLLOW ME

Follow me, across the wide, wide ocean.
Follow me, to where it meets the sand
and I'll show you a place that I've dreamt of all my days.
Follow me, to Bonnie Scotland.

Follow me, to where the heather blossoms.
Come and see the beauty of the isles.
Where the eagle flies high and you'll hear the seagull cry,
follow me, come follow me.

There may be countries far across the sea,
wealthy in silver and gold.
But, to my eye, there's no money that could buy
this land, on which my heart's sold.

Follow me, across the wide, wide ocean.
Follow me, to where it meets the sand,
and I'll show you a place that I've dreamt of all my days.
Follow me, to Bonnie Scotland.

Tho' the way may be long,
there's a promise in the song.
Follow me, to the land I love.
Follow me, follow me, to the land I love.

*A lively song, dedicated to the stream of Scots who return to Scotland
each year on a visit from their new home in foreign lands, and to their
children, visiting Scotland for the first time.*

Words and Music
by Ben Kelly

FOLLOW ME

Arranged by
Alan Kitchen

HIGHLAND CATHEDRAL

VERSE 1.

Land of our fathers, we will always be
faithful and loyal to our own country.
In times of danger, we will set you free.
Lead you to glory and to victory.

VERSE 2.

Hail, Caledonia, to our ancient prayer.
In this Highland Cathedral, let our standards, bare.
Joining, together, with one dream to share.
God bless the people of this land so fair.

CHORUS

Gone is the past, let us start anew.
Let this hope of peace, always remain.
Spirit of Scotia, be strong and true.
Then you children will smile again, again, again, again.

VERSE 3.

Rise, Caledonia, let your voices ring
in this Highland Cathedral of our God and King.
Whom, joy and liberty, to all, will bring.
Come, let your heart, with love and courage, sing.

CHORUS

Lonely the exile, o'er distant seas,
The home of their birth, gone from their eyes.
Bring back their souls o'er the ocean breeze
to the land where their fathers lie.

REPEAT LAST VERSE.

*This was inspired after hearing a wonderful pipe-tune, amazingly written
by two Germans. The words and music emphasise the feeling of a
National Anthem, as intended. The story goes that, under the reign of
King James I of Scotland and England, all clan chiefs were asked to meet
in a secret place, the Highland Cathedral, to pledge an ending to their
constant feuding, and live in peace. This they did and peace reigned in
Scotland and England but, alas, only for as long as the king lived.*

Music by U.Roever & M.Korb
Words by Ben Kelly

HIGHLAND CATHEDRAL

Piano Arrangement
by Alan Kitchen

Slowly and proudly

Land of my fathers we will al- ways be,
faith-ful and loy-al to our own coun-try. In times of dan-ger we will set you free
lead you to glory and to vic- to-ry. Gone is the past, let us start a-new. Let this
hope of peace al- ways re -main. Spir- it of Sco- tia be strong and true then your

ST. KILDA

VERSE 1.

There was a time when the sea was so rich
and the land gave a harvest so full.
Time then, stood still, every glen, every hill,
for the love of the folk from St. Kilda.

CHORUS

Then they took us away, on the mainland, to stay.
Though we promised, one day, to return.
Now the years have gone by, the homeless ruins still lie,
and the warm peat-fires, no longer, burn.
(reprieve)and lain there to rest
in the seas of the west,
is the love of the folk from St. Kilda.

VERSE

At one with the ocean, at one with the wind
and never a harsh word we cried.
But, still, we were beaten, removed from our land.
It was then that St. Kilda, died.

CHORUS

(reprieve)The eagle still flies
over Scotland's blue skies,
but, no more, o'er the grave of St. Kilda

Situated 100 miles off the west coast of Scotland, St. Kilda was visited, in the 1920's, by the folk from the mainland who were amazed to discover that life, on the island, hadn't changed for over 100 years. By 1930, the island had been evacuated and so ended the harsh but incredible survival of St. Kildan people. At the time of writing, only six original St. Kildans are still living.

Words and Music
by Ben Kelly

ST. KILDA

Arranged by
Alan Kitchen

There was a time when the sea was so rich and the land gave a har- vest so full Time, then, stood still, ev-ery glen, ev- ery hill, for the love of the folk from St. Kil- da. Then they

23

WISH I WAS HOME

<u>**VERSE 1.**</u>

I miss the hills, from where the rivers, run.
Down to the glen, they find their way.
I miss the trees, in autumn colours, burn.
Under the sky, they gently sway.
I miss the true love, I left behind.
She made me happy, she eased my mind.
But, now, there's nowhere left to roam.
Wish I was with her, wish I was home.

<u>**VERSE 2.**</u>

And all the laughter that I used to know,
I watched it fade, I watched it go.
Where there's no laughter, loneliness is near,
and Winter lasts all through the year.
But in my homeland, my heart did shine.
And I remember when she was mine.
She walks the hill-side, where reindeer roam,
Wish I was with her, wish I was home.

Written whilst living in London and taking into consideration the home-sick feelings of the many Scots I met there.
A Scot's more a Scot when he's far away from home!

WISH I WAS HOME

I miss the hills from where the ri- vers run. Down to the glen they find their way. I miss the trees, in aut- umn co- lours burn. Un- der the sky they gent- ly

my heart did shine, and I re- mem-ber when she was mine. She walks the hill- side where rein- deer roam, wish I was with her wish I was home, wish I was with her Wish I was home.

THE BALLAD OF RODERICK MACKENZIE

VERSE 1.

The battle was over, the river ran red.
The clans of culloden lay beaten and dead.
But, still, Edwards' army searched here and searched there,
for a price was on the head of Scotlands' true heir.

CHORUS
'Twas brave, young laddie, to forfeit your life
and leave behind, a love-torn wife.
'Twas brave, young laddie, to foil Edwards' men
and gie Prince Charlie, his freedom.

VERSE 2.
They spied a braw laddie, a-fleeing wi' fright.
'Twas Roderick MacKenzie, a brave Jacobite.
"Tis Charlie, I tell you," the enemy cried
and shot poor MacKenzie, their orders, defied.
CHORUS

VERSE 3.
MacKenzie lay bleeding, he knew death was near
and thought to mislead them, his last breath to hear.
"You've killed your own Prince, now collect your reward."
(aside)*"May my king live forever and be free from your sword"*.

CHORUS

This song is based on fact. Whilst patrolling the moors of Cannich, some redcoat soldiers came across Roderick MacKenzie, a fugitive Jacobite. Overkeen to collect the £30000 reward, for the capture of Bonnie Prince Charlie, they shot him. As he lay dying, the soldiers say that, with his red hair and looks, he bore a remarkable likeness to their description of Charlie. Mortally wounded, MacKenzie overheard them and, with his last breath, convinced them that he was, indeed, Prince Charlie.

There were, at the time, Jacobite prisoners held in Ft. Augustus and London, who were willing to identify the Prince, but only if his head remained on his shoulders. The redcoats, unaware of this agreement, cut off MacKenzies' head to make travelling easier.
True to their word, the prisoners at Ft. Augustus would not comment on the decapitated head and, by the time it had reached London, it had decomposed beyond recognition. Consequently, the soldiers collected nothing and the delay allowed the real Prince to make his escape.

Words and Music
by Ben Kelly

Arranged by
Alan Kitchen

THE BALLAD OF RODERICK MACKENZIE

brave, young lad-die to for- feit your life and leave be-

hind a love- torn wife. 'Twas brave, young lad-die to

foil Ed- wards men and gie___Prince Char- lie his free-

dom dom, and gie___Prince Char- lie his free- dom.

I'VE HAD SO MANY GIRLFRIENDS

VERSE 1.
Oh, I've had so many girlfriends, I wouldnae like to say.
I've flirted with every bit of skirt that's ever passed my way.
But now I am regretting playing these foolish games,
for, although I remember the faces well, I never remember their names.

CHORUS
There was Jean or was it Jeannie, or June or Jane or Jan.
Oh, why I forget the girls I've met, I'll never understand.
There was Meg or was it Maggie or even Margaret.
A name so classy for a lassie, how could I forget?

VERSE 2.
Oh, when I see a pretty girl gaze at me, with love,
I cannae help but help masel to what she's thinking of.
But then, as some weeks later, when walking her back home,
just what to call her just slips my mind and I am left alone.

CHORUS
There was Kath or was it Cathy, or Kate or Katherine.
There's what's her name and thingamabob, oh, there I go again.
There was Rose, no, she was Rosie, or maybe RoseMarie.
Whatever the name, it's just the same, I've lost my memory.

PATTER CHORUS
There was Sally-Ann, Susan, Susanah, Samantha
and Sheila and Sheena and Sue.
Eleanor, Ellen, Eliza, Elizabeth, Irene and Eileen too.
Ann and Annie and Anne (with an E), Norma and Nora and Nell.
Some old, some new, but who is who, I guess I'll never tell.
But now I'm wed, it can be said, maybe it's just as well!

This witty song is meant to take, to the extreme, the sometimes, typical experiences of young men in the prime of their youth.

Words and Music
by Ben Kelly

I'VE HAD SO MANY GIRLFRIENDS

Arranged by
Alan Kitchen

34

Chorus

names. There was Jean, or was it Jean-nie or June or Jane or Jan. Oh!

why I for-get the girls I've met, I'll nev- er un- der- stand. There was Meg, or was it

Maggie or ev- en Mar- gar- et. A name so clas- sy for a las- sie,

how could I for- get.

THE LAST FERRY TO SKYE

VERSE 1.
I've travelled this country for many a year and happy with all that I've seen.
From the borders of Tweedale to John O'Groats pier,
from Islay to old Aberdeen.
But now there are places I don't recognise
and the roads lead to I don't know where.
So I am returning to my paradise, I know I'll be happier there.

CHORUS
And I'll be on the last ferry to Skye,
on the last boat to cross the white foam.
To the world and its' fortunes, good-bye.
I'm going back to Dunvegan, my home.

VERSE 2.
Now there are cities, where, once, there were towns
and moorland, where forests once reigned.
And motorways roam where we, once, trod a path.
Were we just children, then?
Now I'm returning while time will allow, an old man to spend his last days,
remembering the Scotland engraved on his brow,
of life in the old-fashioned ways.

CHORUS
And I'll be......

VERSE 3.
They're building a bridge, now, and taking away,
the memory of good days gone by.
When taking the ferry was nought but a laugh, going over the sea to Skye.
She was good enough for Charlie and she's good enough for me,
and when the day comes for our journeys end,
alone, I shall gaze 'cross the wide, empty sea
and I know I shall sea her again.

CHORUS
And I'll be......

*At the time of writing, the bridge over to Skye has not yet been built. Some
islanders welcome it, but some of the older people reckon it will destroy the
island in many ways. But it is the loss of the ferry that most will miss. Filled
with cars and cattle, tourists and tradesmen, whisky and song. The steady pace
and rhythm of the ferry boat amidst the hectic pace of life is an experience
that, sadly, one day, will be forgotten.*

Words and Music
by Ben Kelly

Arranged by
Alan Kitchen

THE LAST FERRY
TO SKYE

HIGHLAND CRADLE SONG

VERSE 1.

Hush now, don't cry, my bairnie.
What tears are these that keep ye from sleep?
Lie still, in peace, my bairnie.
Hush now, and don't ye weep.

CHORUS

The nightingale sings,
o'er moorland it brings
a song on its' wings,
in the silence of night.
The mountain so tall,
the field-mouse so small,
in slumber, will fall,
till morning light.

VERSE 2.

Hush now, don't cry, my bairnie.
What makes ye sad and wantin' tae weep?
Dream happy dreams, my bairnie,
safe in your silent sleep.

CHORUS

*The voice and piano version of this song can be found on an earlier page
in the book. In this instrumental/voice version, I have tried to show that it
is possible to use the much maligned sound of the pipes to lull a child to
sleep, as would have been the case, many years ago.*

Words by
Ben Kelly

HIGHLAND CRADLE SONG
(Instrumental)

Music Trad.
Arranged by
Alan Kitchen